THE TELEPHONE
Doodle
Book

THE TELEPHONE
Doodle Book

ANDREW PINDER

Michael O'Mara Books Limited

First published in Great Britain in 2009 by
Michael O'Mara Books Limited
9 Lion Yard
Tremadoc Road
London SW4 7NQ

A CIP catalogue record for this book is available from the British Library.

Papers used by Michael O'Mara Books Limited are natural, recyclable products
made from wood grown in sustainable forests. The manufacturing processes
conform to the environmental regulations of the country of origin.

ISBN: 978-1-84317-358-8

1 2 3 4 5 6 7 8 9 10

Design by Design 23

Printed and bound in Finland by WS Bookwell, Juva

www.mombooks.com

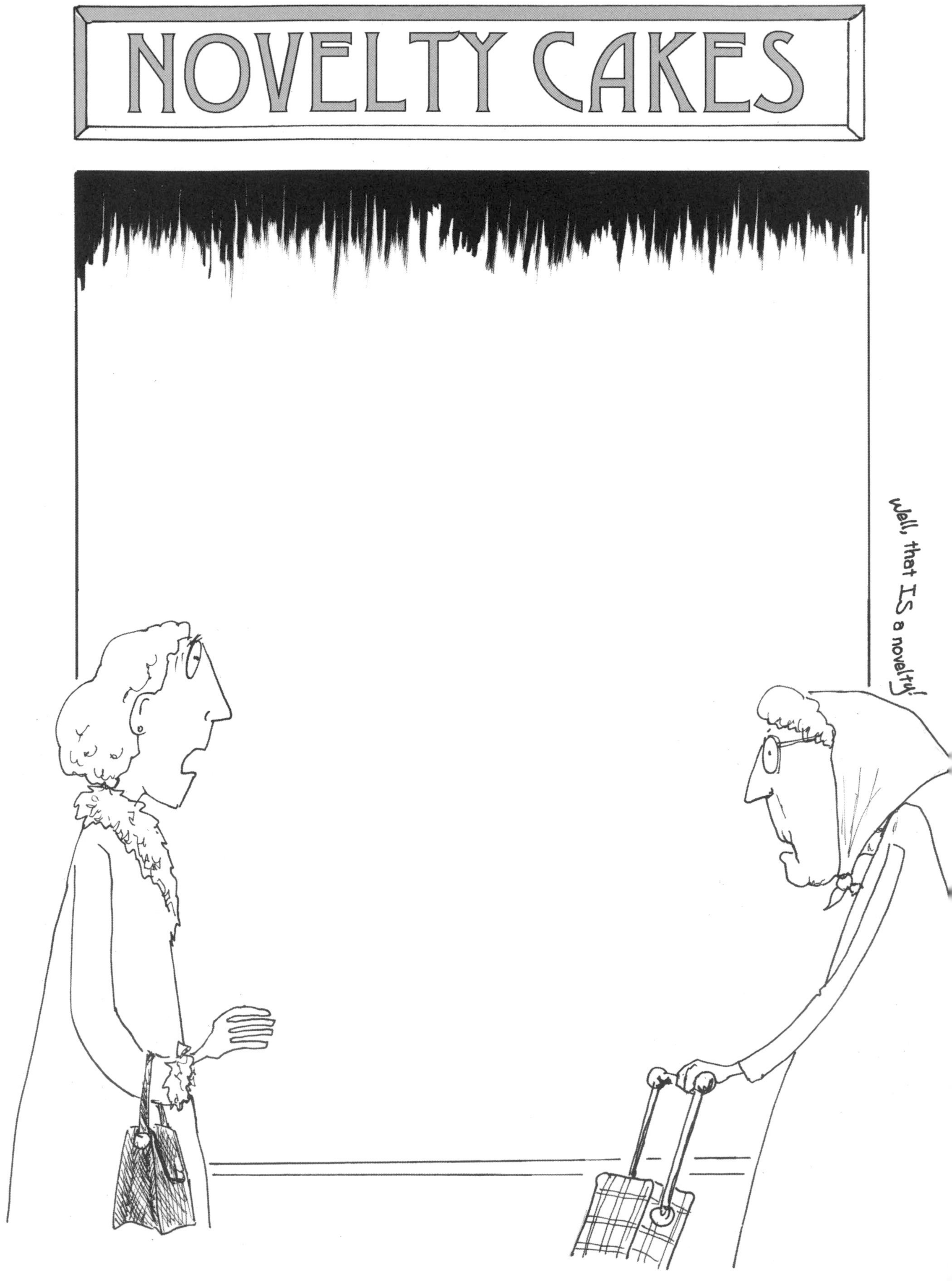
NOVELTY CAKES
Well, that IS a novelty!

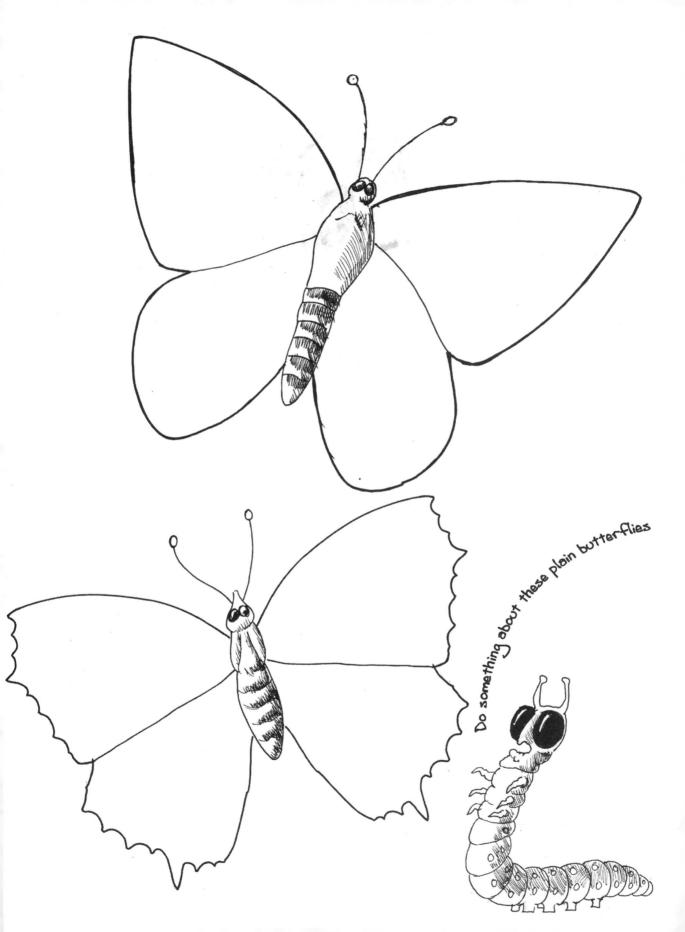

Do something about these plain butterflies

What the butler saw!

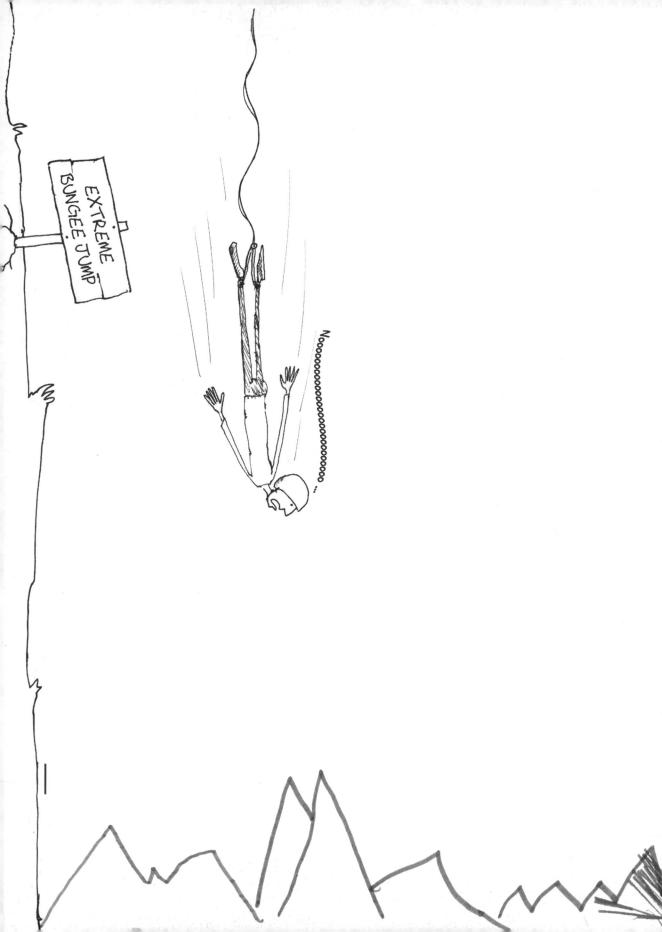

Ladies and gentlemen, please decorate your balloons.

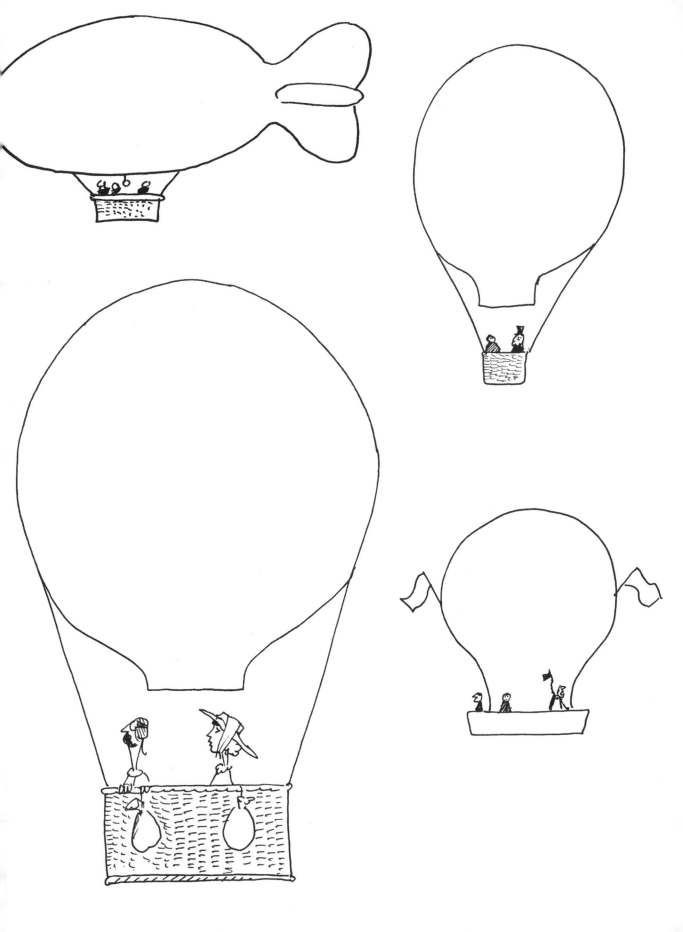

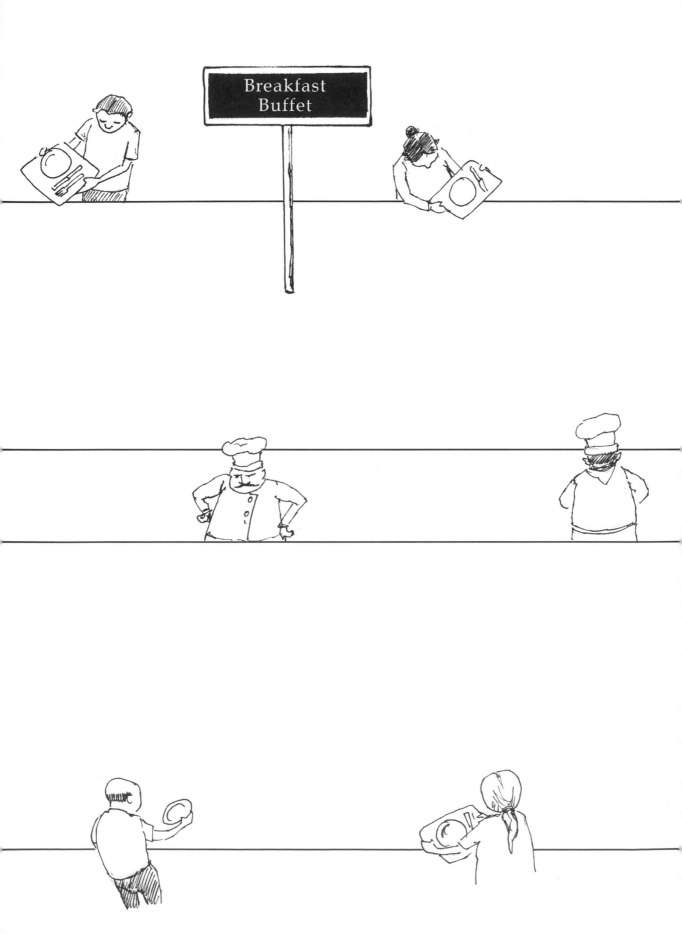

Careful, I'm sure that I heard something move in that box ...

Alien autopsy

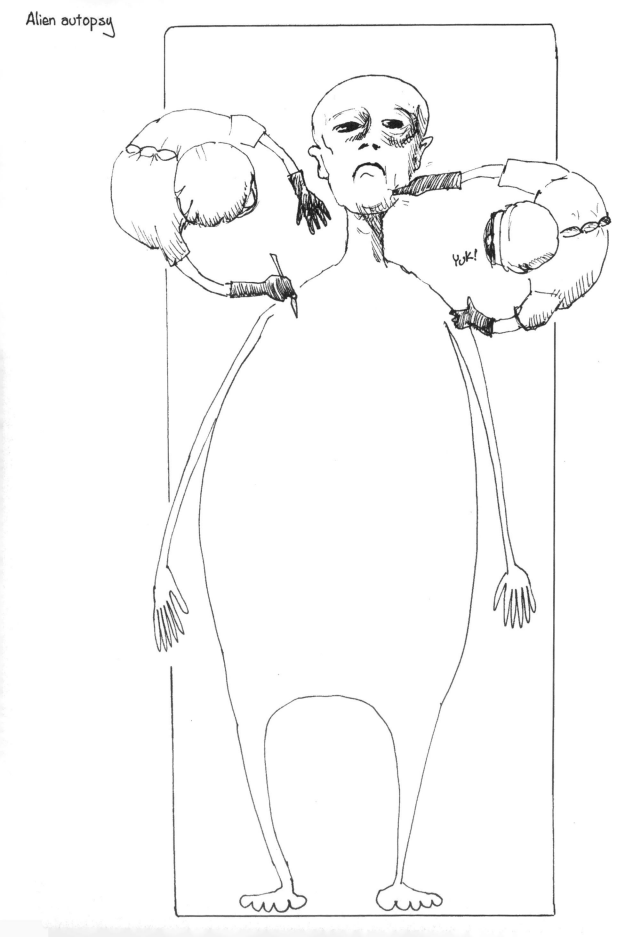

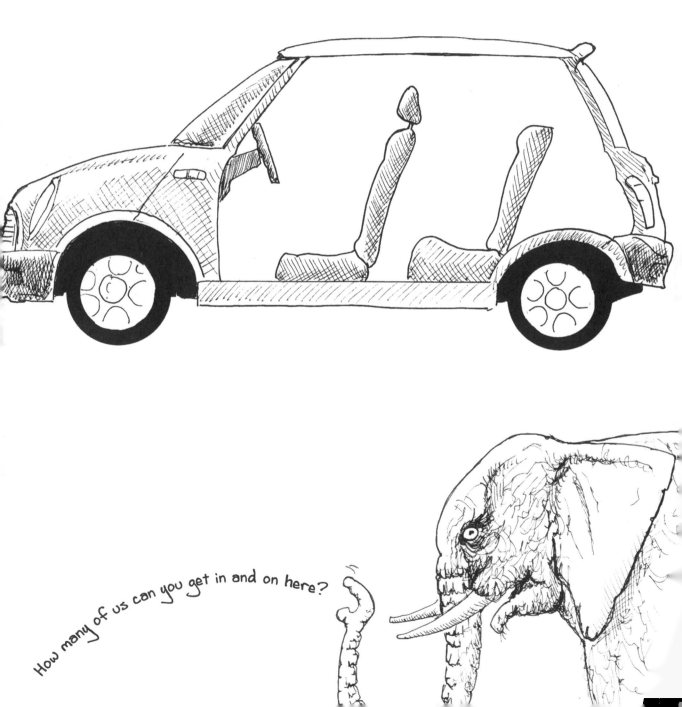

How many of us can you get in and on here?

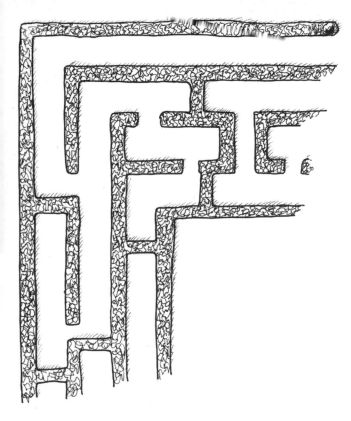

Finish
the maze

A			N
B			O
C			P
D			Q
E			R
F			S
G			T
H			TH
I			U
J			V
K			W
L			X
M			Y
			Z

Write like an Egyptian.

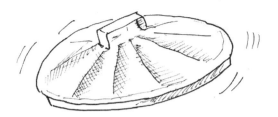

What's in the dustbin?

Yeah, I know, but they're good earners.

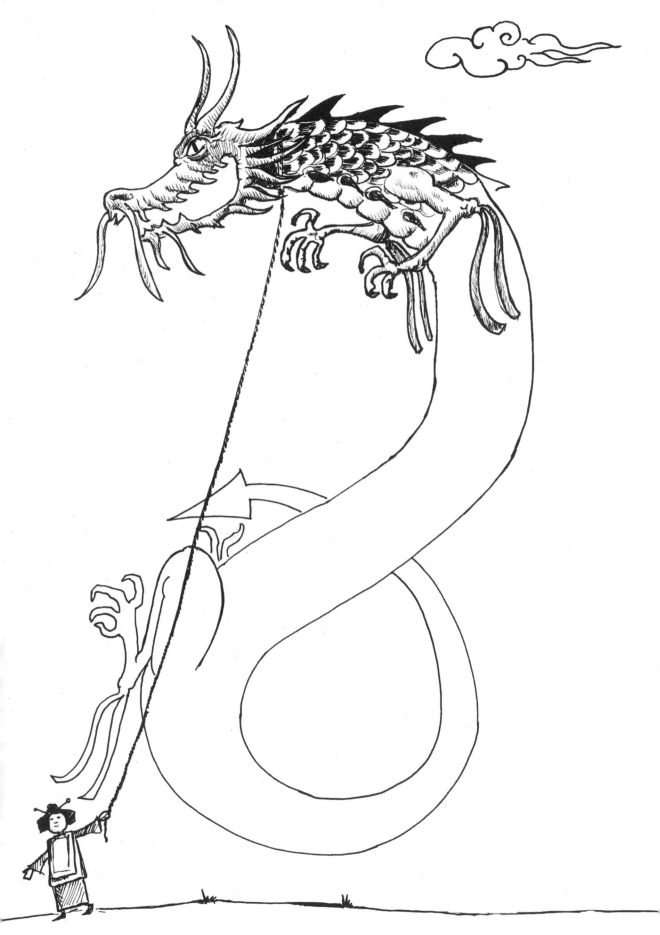

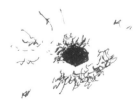

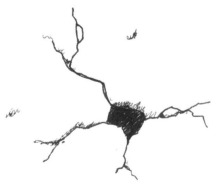

Fill the page with doves and ravens

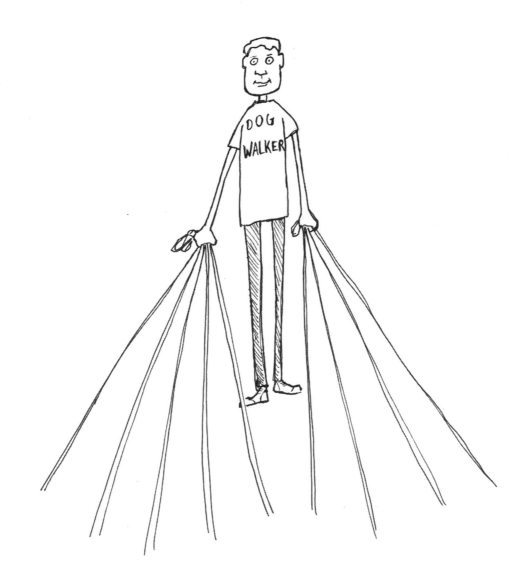

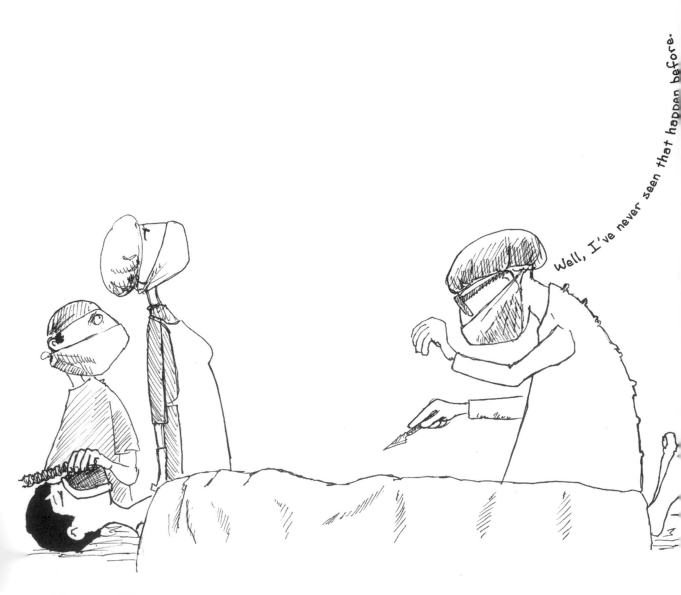

There's always someone who has to go over the top with his crest.

What worries me is, I'm not sure that new one is a bird.

Formation flying bats!

CONTEMPORARY ART FAIR

THE
WORLD'S
UGLIEST
FISH

Fill yer trolley.

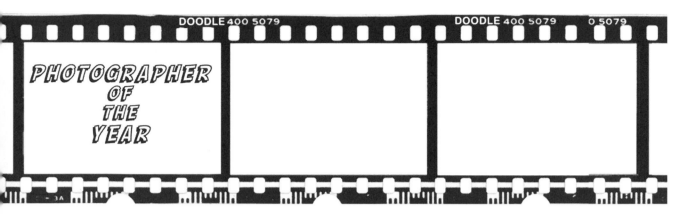

PHOTOGRAPHER
OF
THE
YEAR

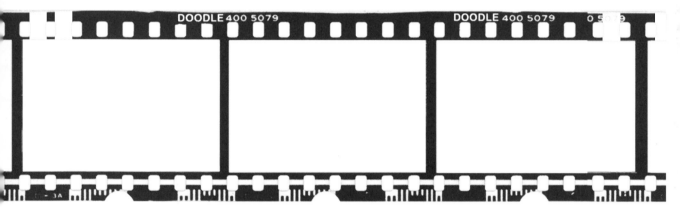

Good grief! What's Simpson got on?

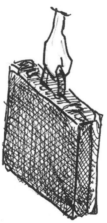

Doodle a background, then camouflage the chameleon.

Finish the medieval town.

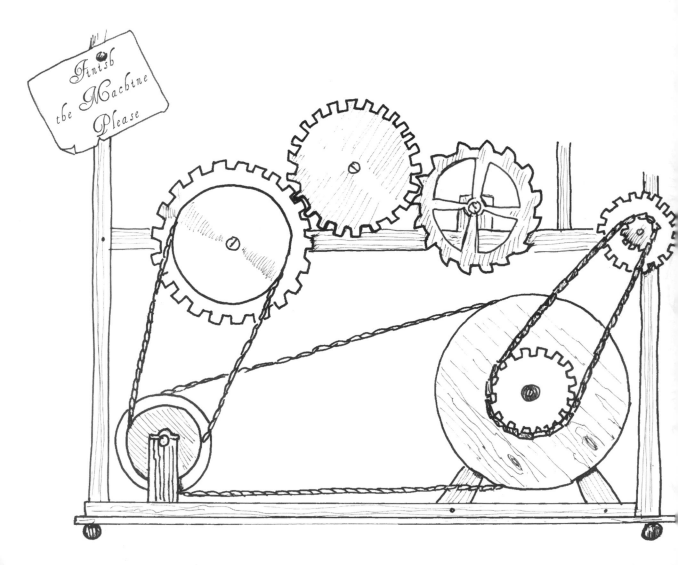

hhhhut!

At last, the lost city of ...Ahhggg...

If dogs ruled the world ...

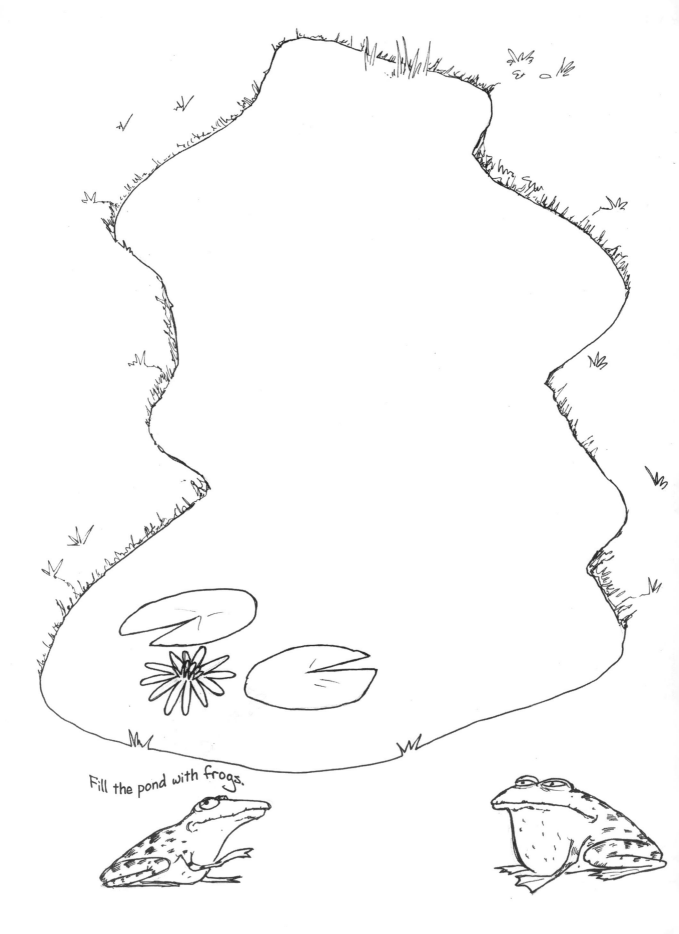

Fill the pond with frogs.

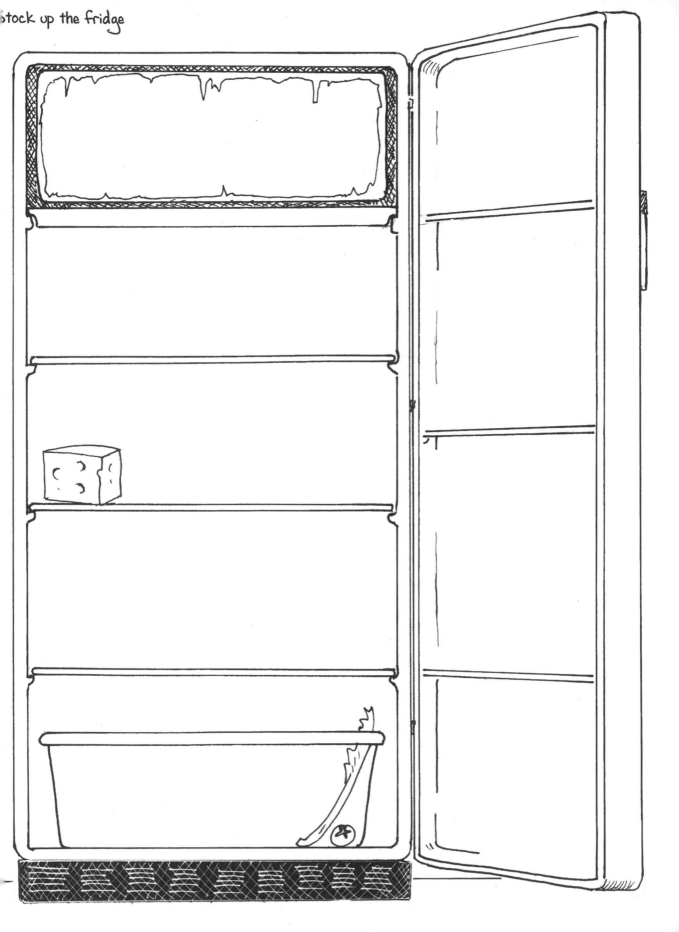

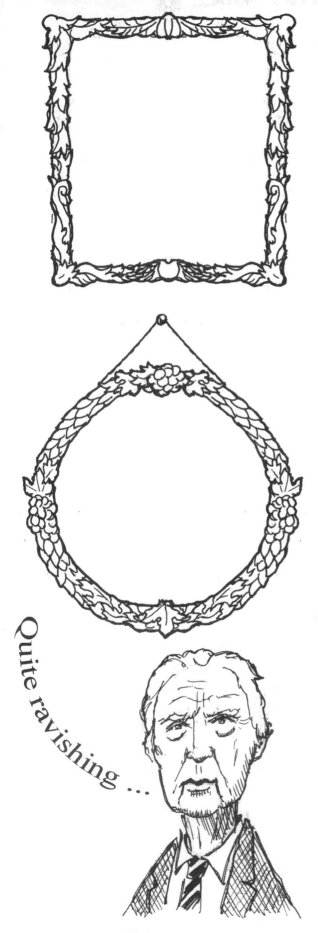

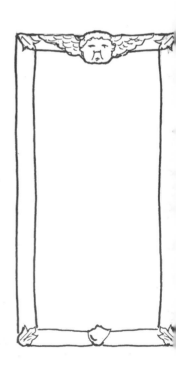

Quite ravishing ...

Fill the forest.

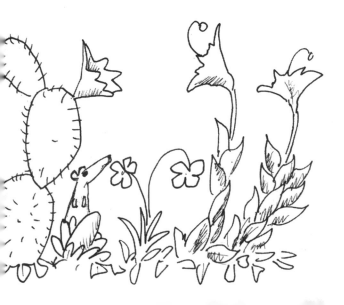

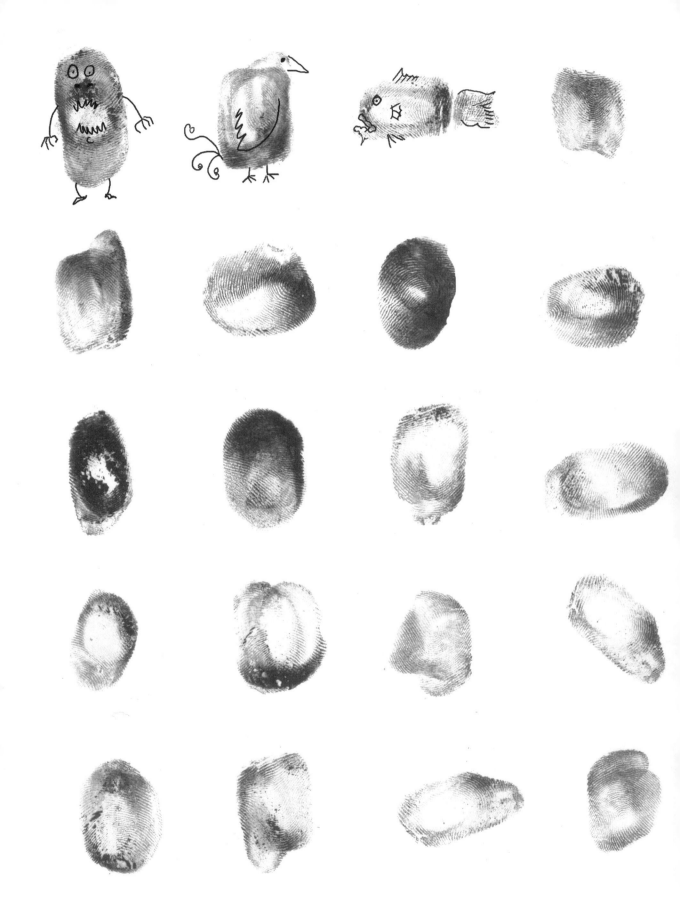

What's on the telly?

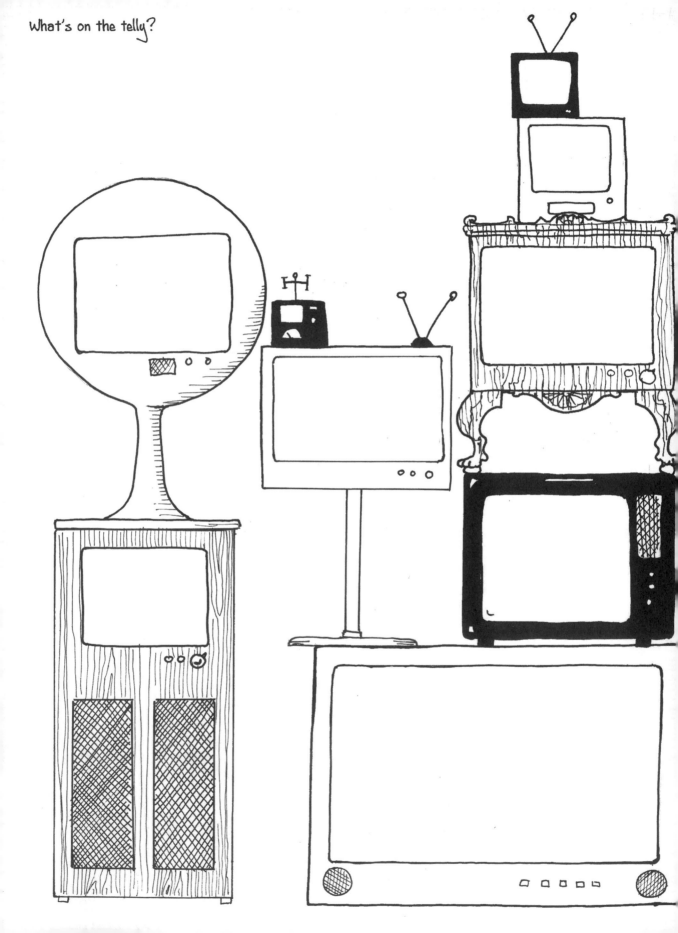

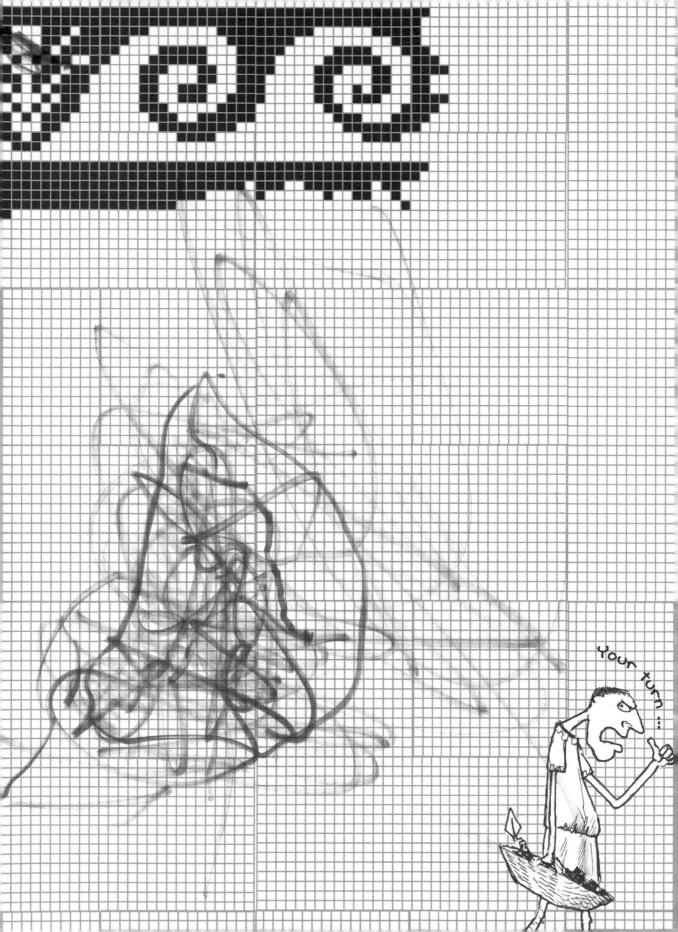

Your turn ...

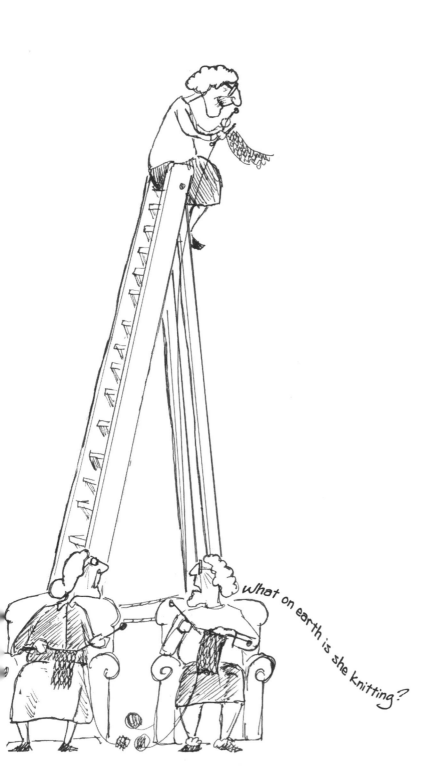

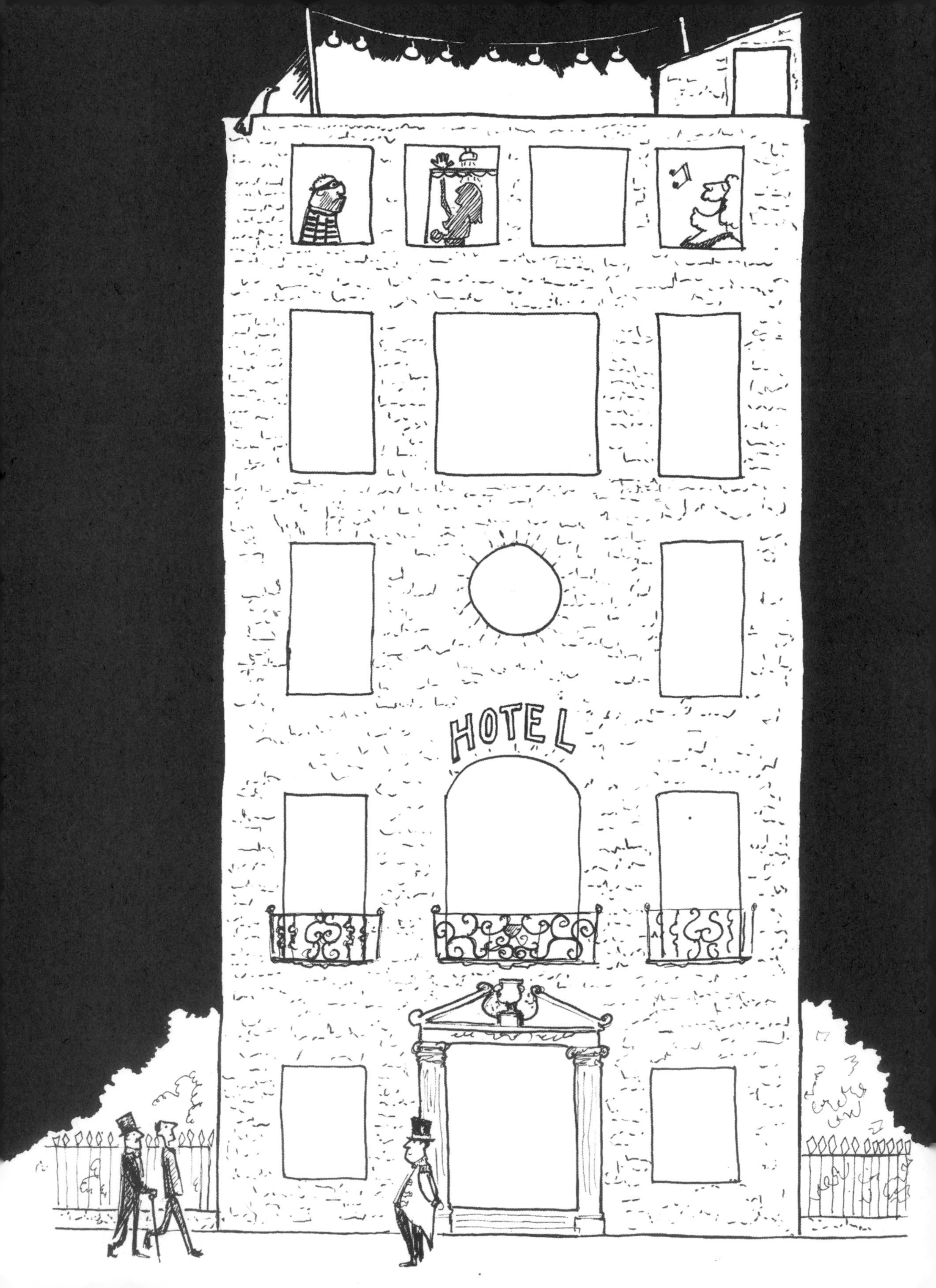
HOTEL

Give us some hair!

What's next?.

.. th≡ d●●rs?

Finish the embroidery.

Let's decorate these lovely Christmas balls.
NICELY!

Where is all the cherry blossom?

Illuminate these Letters

How many turkeys escape the farm?

Decorate our camper van

Finish the carpet

Design a series of stamps.

Ufff! What 'orrible plain fans.

Winter	Summer	Winter	Summer	Winter	

What's in Reception?

Come on, chop chop, get it finished!

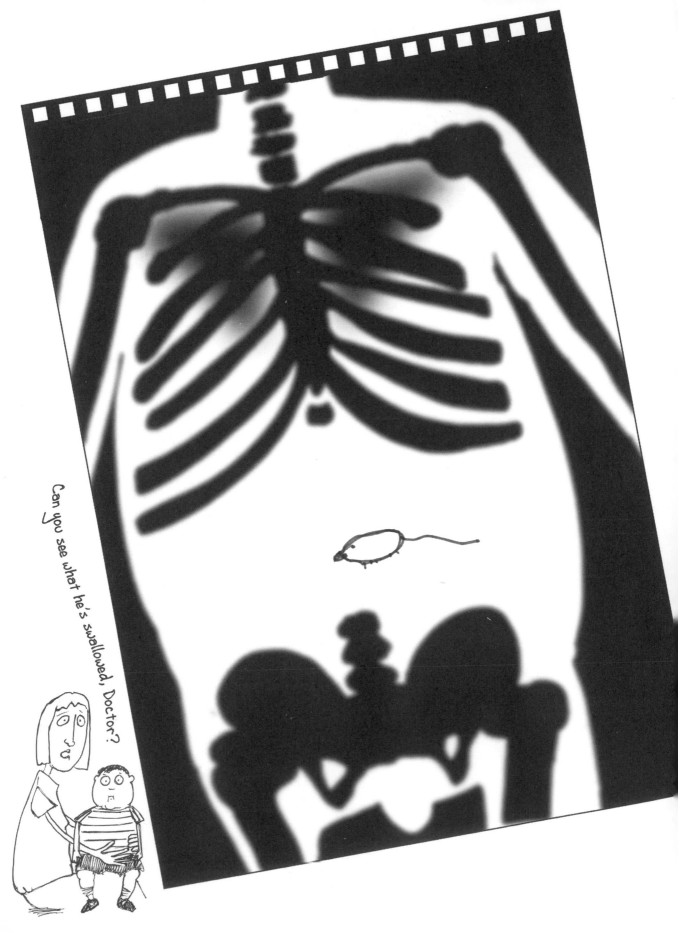

What's the starlet wearing to the Awards?

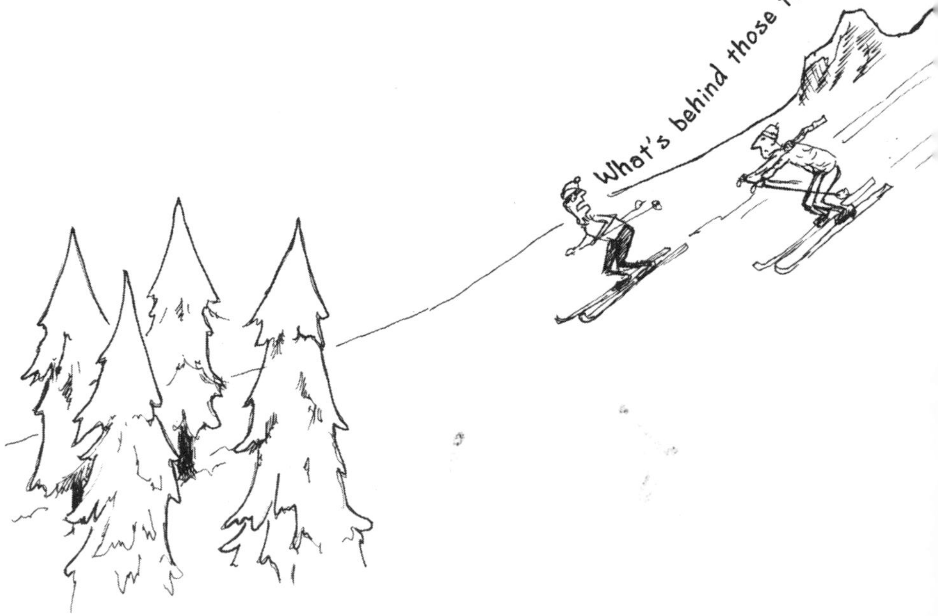
What's behind those trees?

Finish the procession.

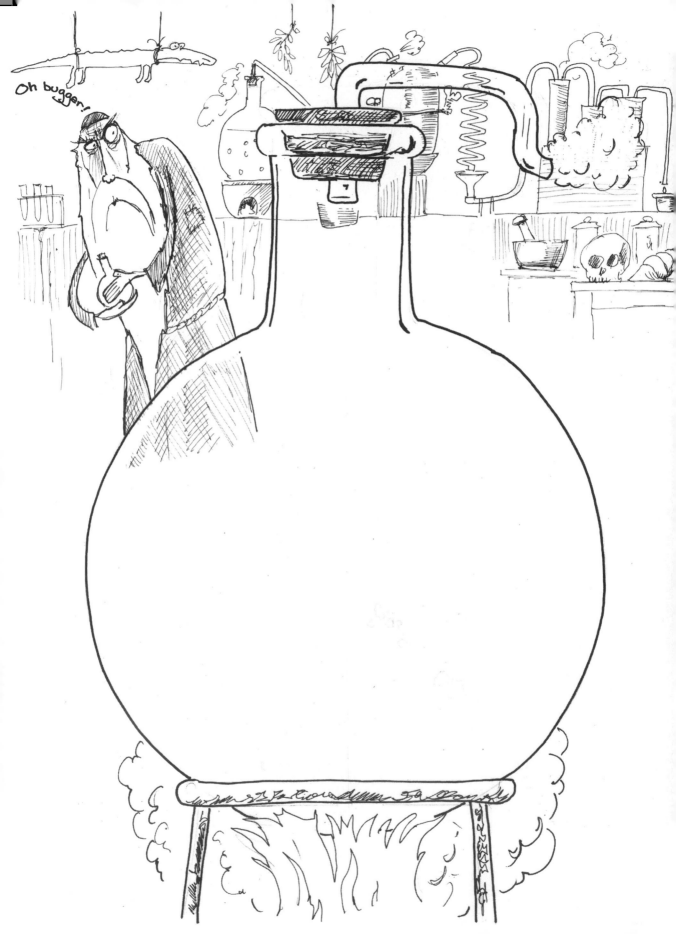

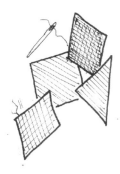

Finish ma quilt.

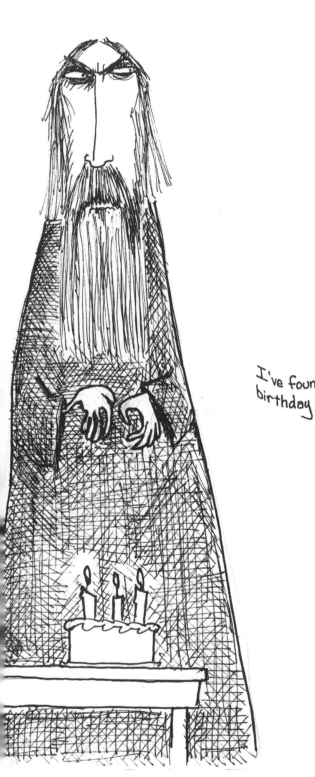

I've found the perfect birthday present for Rasputin.

Stripes please.

How many sunbathers on the beach?

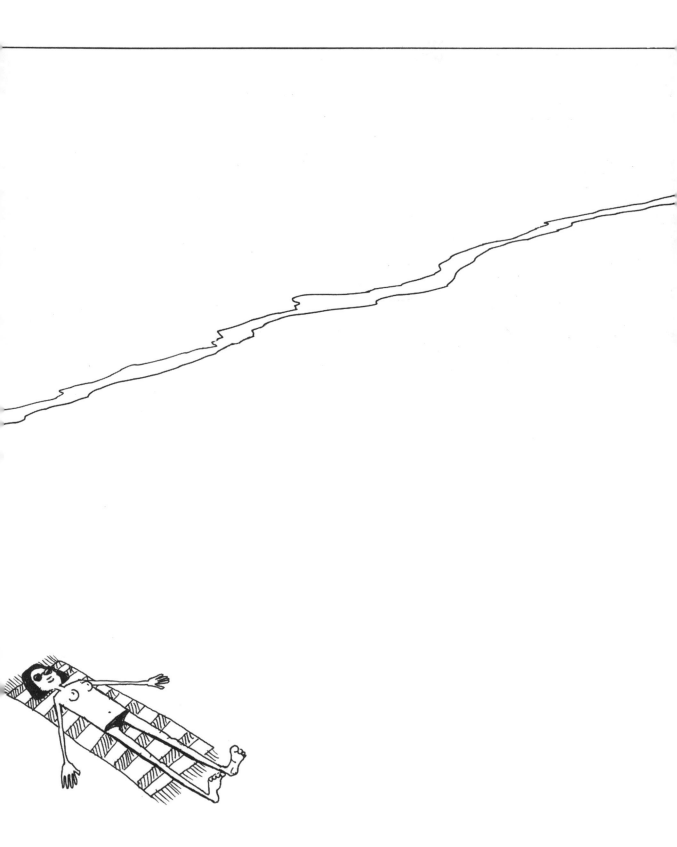

Very clever, now fill the page ...

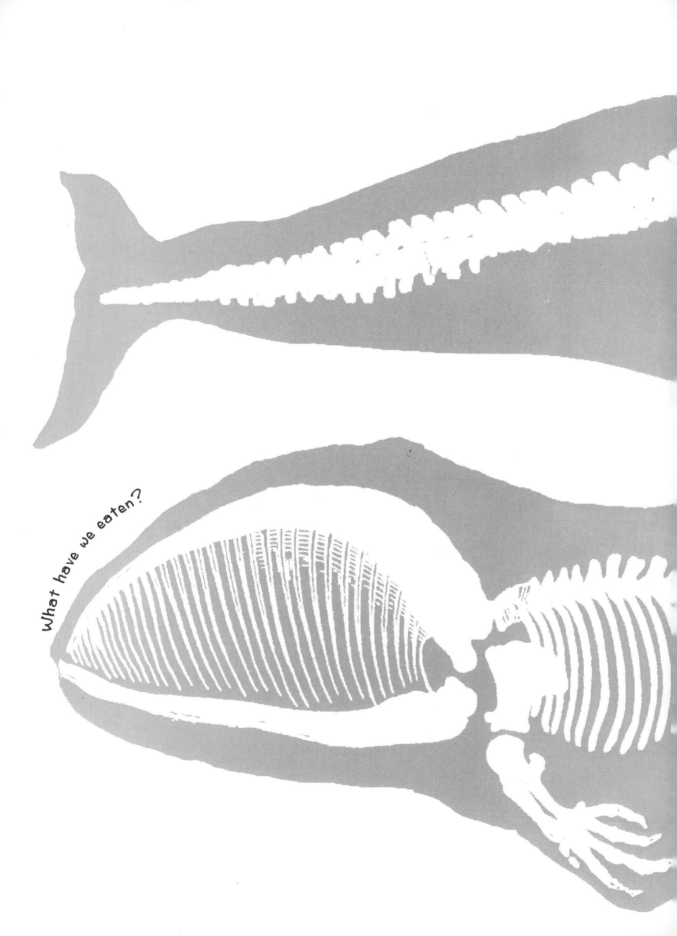

What have we eaten?

Silence, Watson, we will soon have our killer.

and over there a big gazebo covered in roses.

How many cats has the cat-lady got today?

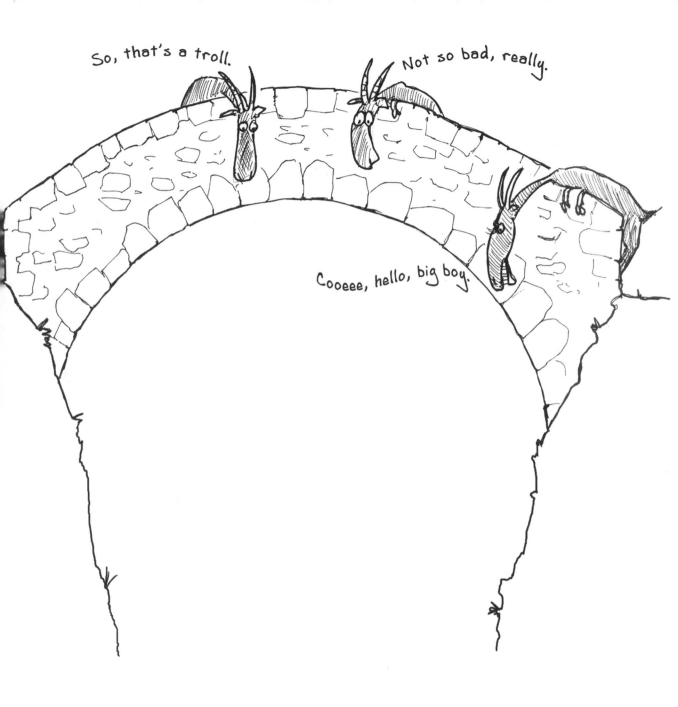

Someone's always got to go one better.

PUMPKIN COMPETITION

Quick, he hasn't got his gun, everyone into the field!

Come on, hurry up, what's up there?

Cabinet of Curiosities

Create a gorilla